PAGES
2-3

KV-315-251

PAGE 5

PAGE 8

7 4 11 9

PAGES
10-11

PAGE 9

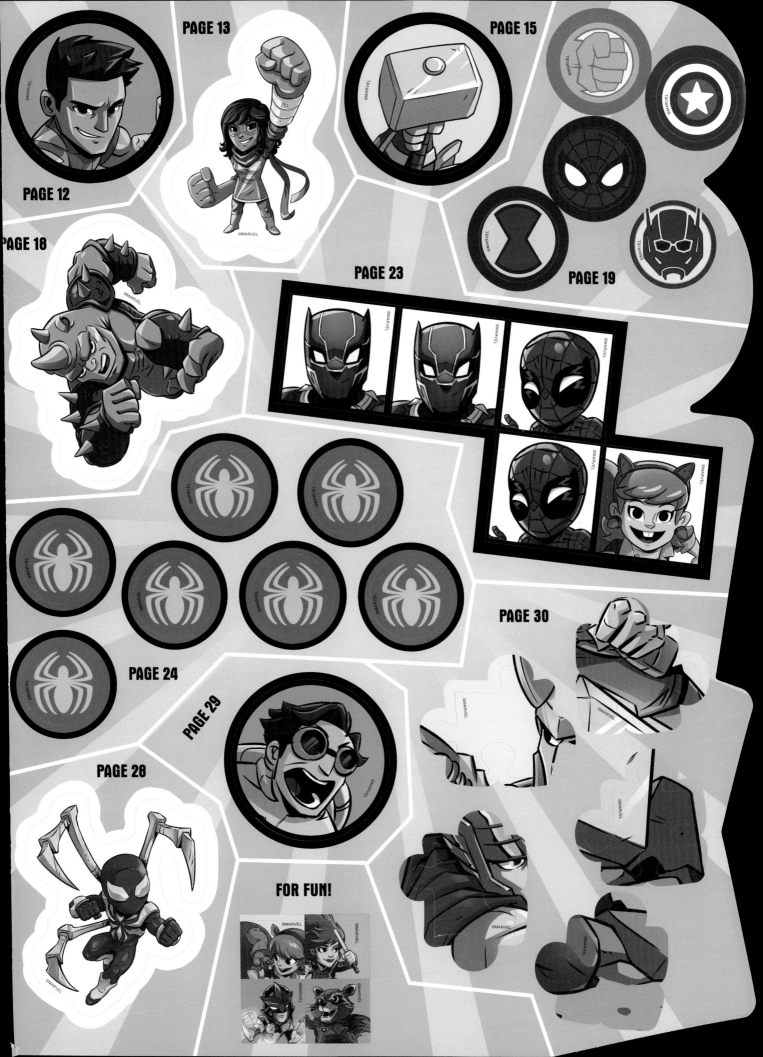

PAGE 13

PAGE 15

PAGE 12

PAGE 18

PAGE 23

PAGE 19

PAGE 30

PAGE 24

PAGE 29

PAGE 28

FOR FUN!

PAGE 32-33

PAGE 34

FOR FUN!

PAGE 36

PAGE 39

PAGE 37

PAGE 44-45

FOR FUN!

HERO ACTIVITIES

Autumn
Publishing

SPIDEY SPOT THE DIFFERENCE

Can you spot six differences between these two pictures of Spider-Man, Kid Arachnid and Spider-Gwen?

Answers on page 47

GREEN DREAM TEAM

Colour the Hulk and She-Hulk in your favourite shade of green.

4

SUPER HERO TEAMMATES

Which one of his Super Hero friends has Iron Man teamed up with to save the day?

IRON MAN'S TEAMMATE...
- Does not have long hair.
- Wears a mask.
- Is not carrying a shield.

ADD A STICKER OF IRON MAN'S TEAMMATE HERE.

Answer on page 47

5

TANGLED WEBS

Thwip, thwip, thwip! Which web is about to trap which villain?

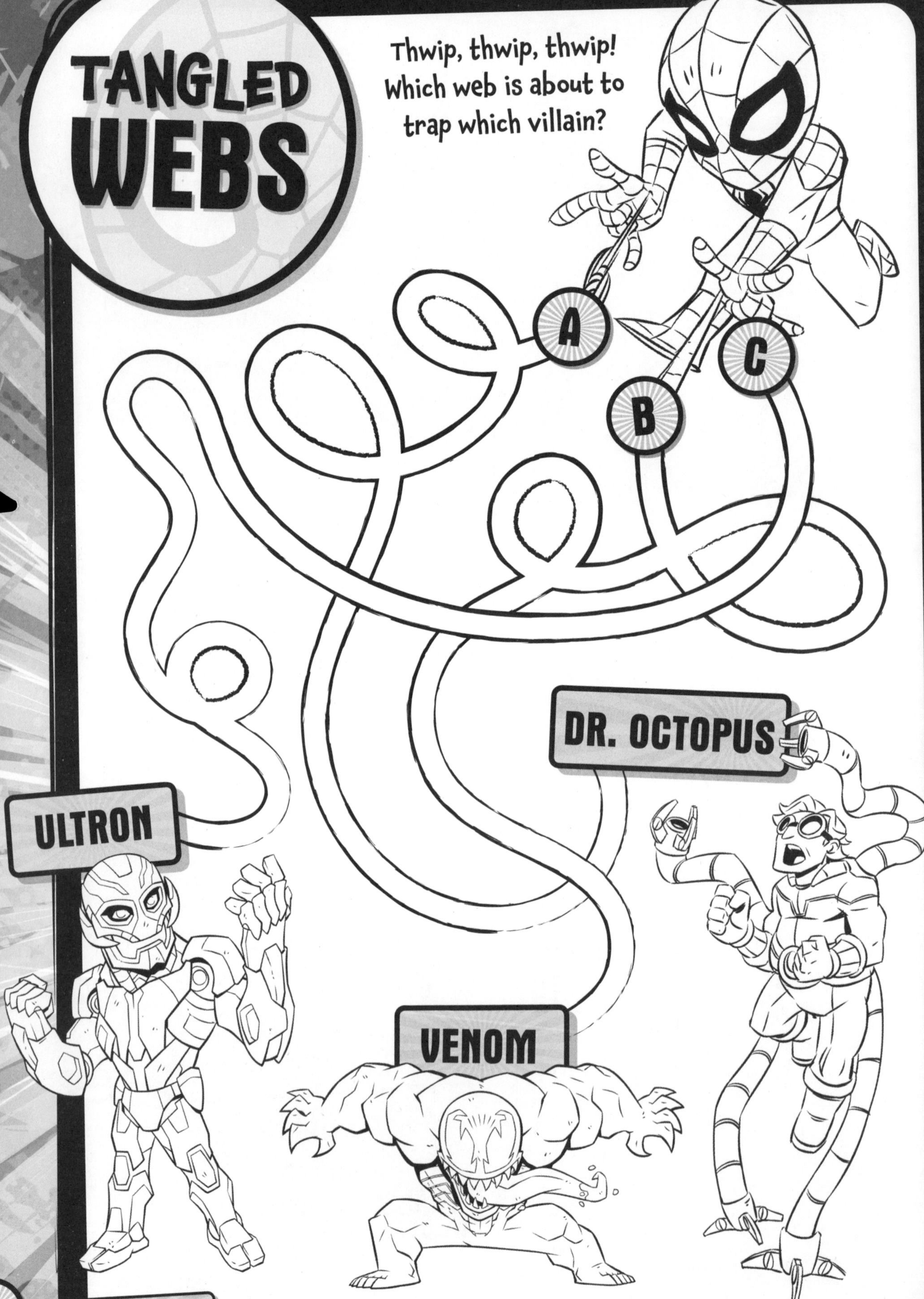

A   B   C

DR. OCTOPUS

ULTRON

VENOM

FALCON SHADOW MATCH

Falcon is ready to soar into action. Which shadow matches our hero exactly?

A

B

C

D

E

Answer on page 47

SUPER VILLAIN SUDOKU

Complete this picture puzzle so that every row and column contains all four villains. Use the stickers to fill the empty spaces.

Answers on page 47

9

HEROES AND VILLAINS

PLAY THIS GAME WITH A FRIEND.

1. Each player chooses to be the hero or the villain.
2. Take it in turns to place your character's sticker on the grid.
3. The first player to get three in a row wins!

GAME 1

GAME 2

10

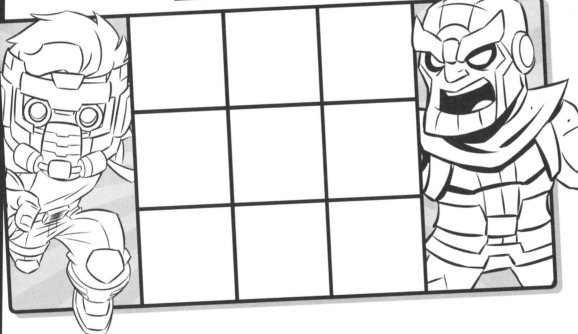

GAME 3

GAME 4

HEROES

VILLAINS

MATCHING REPTILS

Which two of these pictures of Reptil are exactly the same?

A

B

C

D

E

F

ADD A REPTIL STICKER HERE WHEN YOU'VE WORKED IT OUT.

12

Answer on page 47

SUPER HERO MATCH

Draw lines to match the Super Heroes with their super symbols.

A

B

C

D

 **1**

 **2**

 **3**

 **4**

Answers on page 47

MJOLNIR MAZE

Mighty Thor has thrown his hammer, Mjolnir. Guide him through the maze to get it back.

GIVE YOURSELF A STICKER WHEN YOU'VE FINISHED!

START

Answer on page 47

ANT-MAN AND WASP

Colour this picture of Ant-Man and Wasp flying to the rescue.

ODD CAPTAIN MARVEL OUT

Which one of these pictures of Captain Marvel is different from all the rest? Draw a circle around her.

Answer on page 47

17

Black Panther is tracking Rhino down. Which trail should he follow? When you've found the right one, add a sticker of the villain over his outline.

A

B

C

Answer on page 47

SYMBOL SEQUENCE

Find the right stickers to complete these sequences.

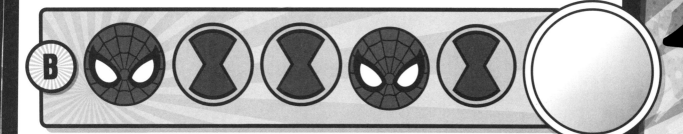

Answers on page 47

SUPER HERO TEAMMATES

Which one of the small pictures on the opposite page matches this big picture of your Super Hero friends?

A

B

C

Answer on page 47

D

21

SUPER HERO SUDOKU

Complete this picture puzzle so that every row and column contains all four of these Super Heroes. Use the stickers to fill the empty spaces.

Answer on page 47

23

NEW YORK CITY MAZE

Guide Spider-Man as he swings through the city streets to find Sandman.

START

FINISH

Answer on page 47

JOIN THE DOTS

Join the dots to complete this picture of the Hulk.

27

IRON SPIDER

Add a sticker of Iron Spider here. Then, use your drawing skills to finish the picture and colour it in.

28

VILLAIN TEAM-UP

Green Goblin is hatching an evil plot, but he needs someone's help. Which villain will he team up with?

GREEN GOBLIN'S CHOSEN VILLAIN...

- Does not have a beard.
- Does not have pointed ears.
- Is wearing shoes.

ADD A STICKER OF THE CHOSEN VILLAIN HERE.

Answer on page 47

INFINITY STONE CHALLENGE

The six Infinity Stones are super-powerful gems, and Thanos is hunting them down. Find all of them hidden in this grid before Thanos beats you to it!

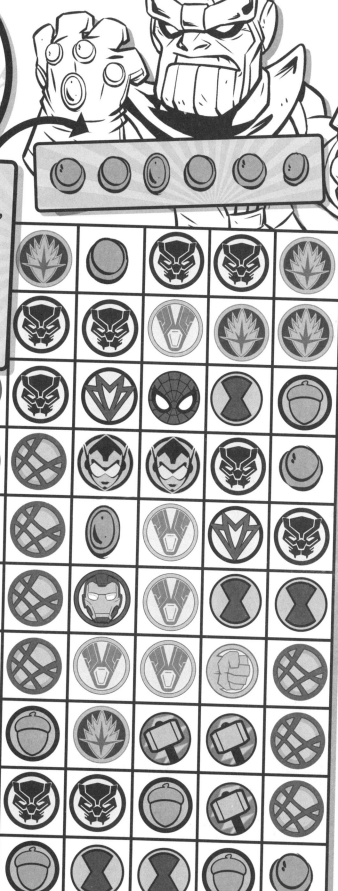

31

Answers on page 48

ADD A STICKER FOR EVERY DIFFERENCE YOU SPOT.

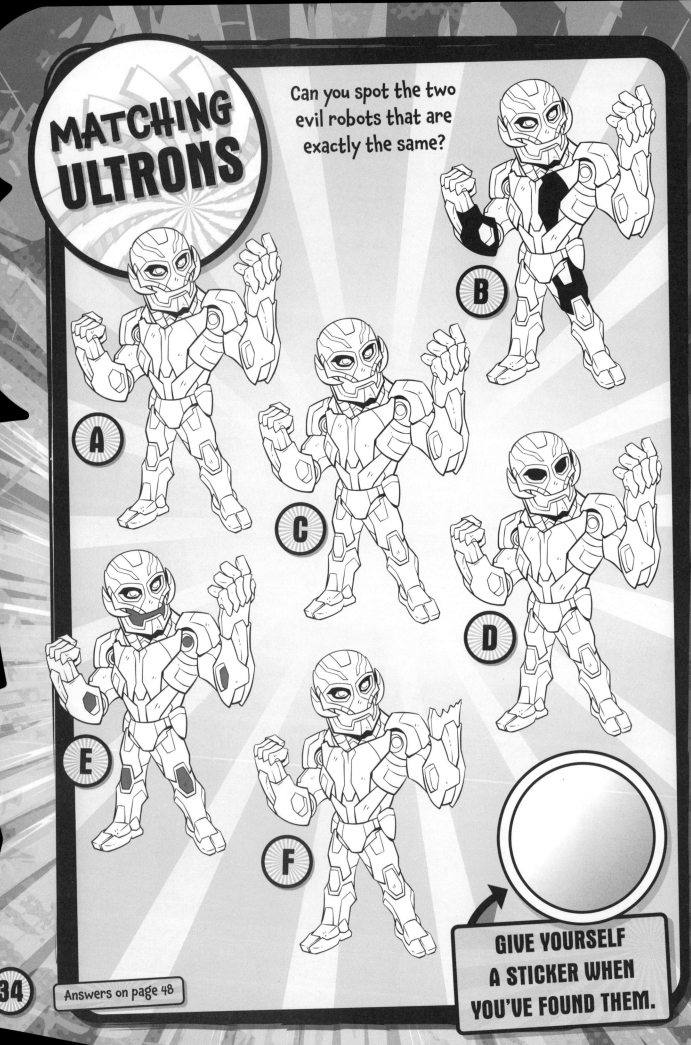

MATCHING ULTRONS

Can you spot the two evil robots that are exactly the same?

A

B

C

D

E

F

GIVE YOURSELF A STICKER WHEN YOU'VE FOUND THEM.

DRAW SPIDER-GWEN

Use the grid to help you draw Spider-Gwen. Then, colour her in!

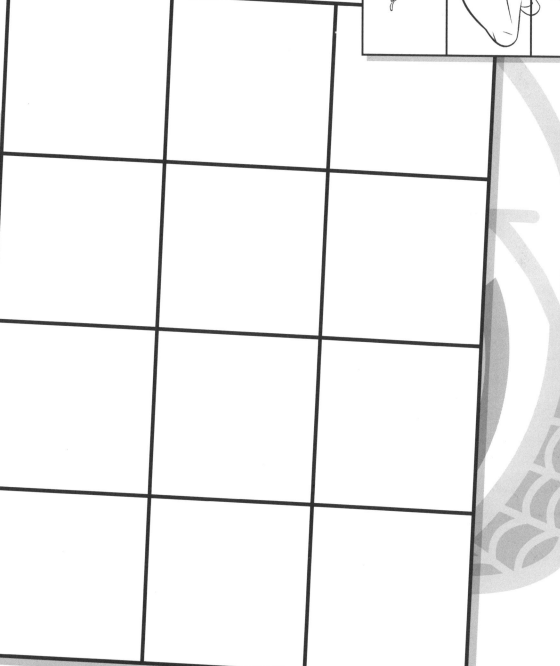

SUPER VILLAIN SEQUENCE

Find the right stickers to complete these villain sequences.

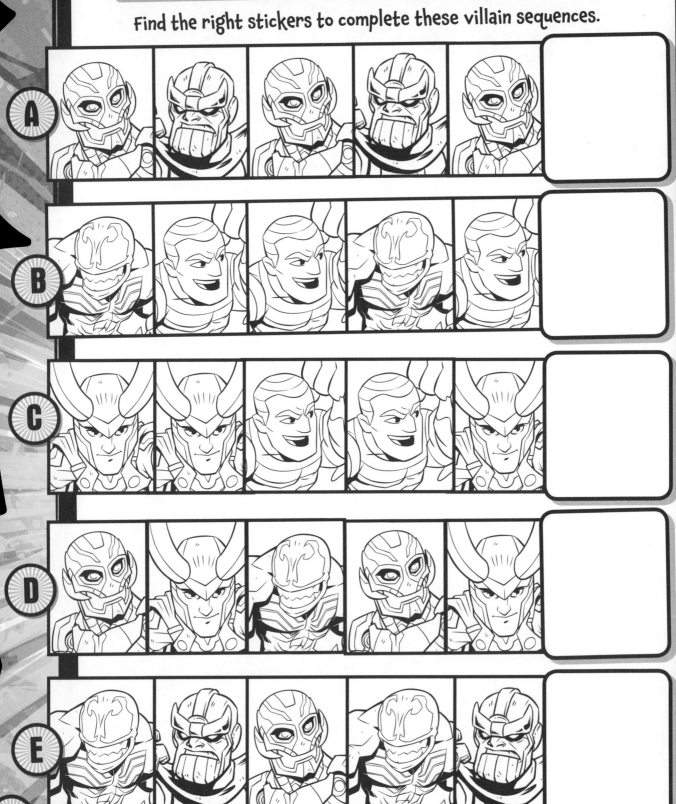

ODD VISION OUT

One of these pictures of Vision is different from all the rest. Which one?

A

B

C

D

E

F

ADD A STICKER HERE WHEN YOU'VE FOUND THE ODD ONE OUT.

Answer on page 48

DOODLE YOUR OWN INVENTION

Tony Stark is a brilliant inventor.
He invented his own Iron Man armour,
repulsor blasts and lots of other things.

Can you invent something amazing for him and draw it here?

NAME: _____

WHAT DOES IT DO? _____

_____

SUPER HERO SEQUENCE

Find the right stickers to complete these Super Hero sequences.

Answers on page 48

READY FOR ANYTHING

Something's missing from this picture of Black Widow. Draw in her batons and colour her in.

STORMY WEATHER

Doodle the lightning storm that Thor is about to create, then colour in the picture.

FLYING HIGH

Iron Man and Captain Marvel make a great team. Which one of the small pictures is the same as the bigger picture of the Super Hero friends?

A

B

C

Answer on page 48

IRON MAN, SIGNING OFF!

See you soon for more heroic adventures!

ANSWERS

Pages 2-3

Page 5
Iron Man's teammate is Black Panther

Page 6
A = DR. OCTOPUS
B = VENOM
C = ULTRON

Page 7
Shadow C matches Falcon exactly

Page 8
There are 7 squirrels

Page 9

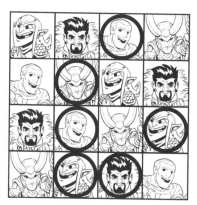

Page 12
Pictures C and E are exactly the same

Page 14
A=4, B=1, C=2, D=3

Page 15

Page 17
Picture B is different

Page 18
Trail C leads to Rhino

Page 19

A =   B =

C =   D =

E =

Pages 20-21
Picture D matches

Page 23

Page 24

Page 25
A=2, B=3, C=1, D=4

Page 26

START

FINISH

Page 29
Green Goblin's chosen villain is Dr. Octopus

47

Page 30

Page 31

Pages 32–33

Page 34
Ultron A and C are
exactly the same

Page 36

A = B = C =

D = E =

Page 37
Picture F is different

Page 39

A = B = C =

D = E =

Page 43
Picture B is the same

Pages 44–45

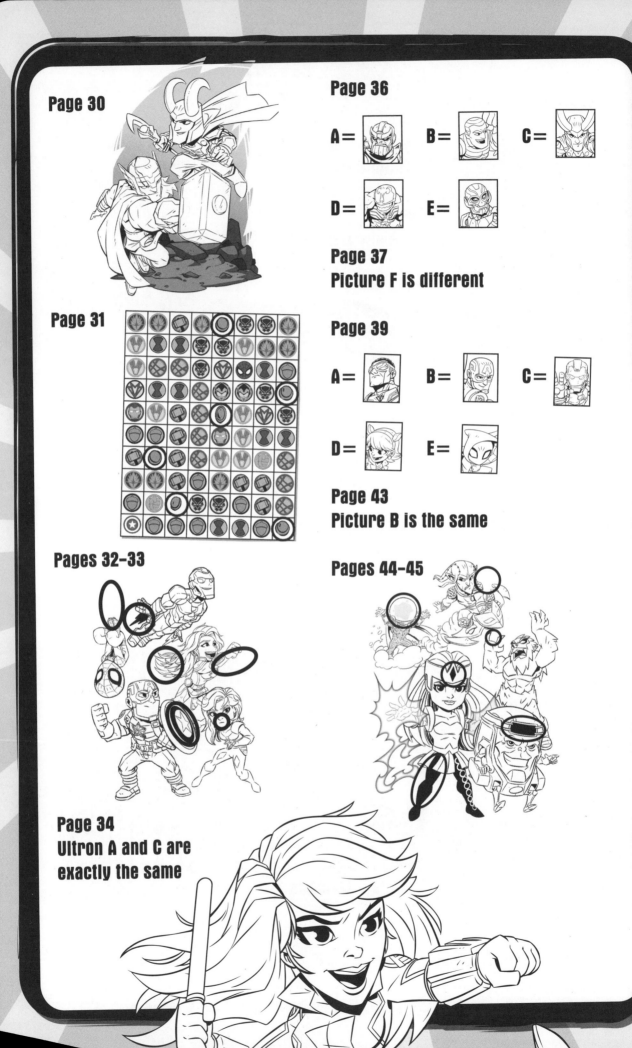